a dog with a boot

a cat

Using this book

Ladybird's *talkabouts* are ideal for encouraging children to talk about what they see. Bold colourful pictures and simple questions help to develop early learning skills — such as matching, counting and detailed observation.

Look at this book with your child. First talk about the pictures yourself, and point out things to look at. Let your child take her* time. With encouragement, she will start to join in, talking about the familiar things in the pictures. Help her to count objects, to look for things that match, and to talk about what is going on in the picture stories.

*To avoid the clumsy use of he/she, the child is referred to as 'she'. **talkabouts** are suitable for both boys and girls.

Published by Ladybird Books Ltd
80 Strand London WC2R ORL
A Penguin Company

1 3 5 7 9 10 8 6 4 2

© LADYBIRD BOOKS MMIII

Printed in Italy

talkabout
On the Farm

written by Lorraine Horsley
illustrated by Alex Ayliffe

Ladybird

Here is the farmer in his den,
With his horse and sheep,
and goat and hen.

6

Who can you see?
What are the animals doing?

Can you quack like a duck
or bark like a dog?
Can you moo like a cow
or croak like a frog?

What noises do the other animals make?

Here is the tractor pulling and ploughing, digging the field and sowing the seed.
Tell the story.

2

3

4

11

Little speckled hen,
Please lay an egg for me.
Little speckled hen,
I'd like one for my tea.

How many eggs are in each nest?
Where is the cockerel?

All the baby animals have lost their way. Can you help them find their mums?

Do you know what the baby
animals are called?

15

Apples and pears, crunchy and sweet,
Grown by the farmer for me to eat.
Tell the story.

What is your favourite fruit?

Find another...

apple

strawberry

tomato

What colour is the strawberry?

Can you find...

one curly tail?

two grey ears?

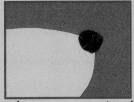

three puppies' noses?

four goats' beards?

21

There's always work to do on
a busy farm.
What jobs need to be done?

Would you like to work on a farm?

Match each animal to its shadow and
description.

I have a
swishy tail.

I have a soft
woolly coat.

I have
fluffy feathers.

I have two
sharp horns.

Tell the story of the duck family.

Find each animal a home.

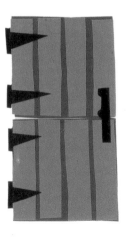

hen house

stable

pig pen

basket

Can you find these as well?

some sheep

a farmer

some cherries